FOREWORD

"The Last Bivalvian" is a wonderful, magical story about a mermaid and the last Bivalvian on their quest to help save the waters of the Chesapeake Bay. This is a great read for all ages to go on the journey with the "Chesapeake Mermaid", and her new found friend "Larvey" as they help to bring clean water awareness, balance to the ecosystem, and to educate others around them on how to help save the bay from pollution and to bring marine life back!

"The Last Bivalvian" truly is an inspiring story that touches our inner melody, which binds all life together in one song. We are all waves of one ocean, and drops of one sea, let's help the Chesapeake Mermaid and Larvey continue the care and protection of our dear Chesapeake Bay. We all can do our part.

— *Vytas Reid, Meteorologist*

Magical Map of the Past

North
West · East
South

Susquehanna R.

Gunpowder R.

Jones Falls

Great Falls

Patapsco

Marsh Organ?

Sassafras R.

Chesapeake Bay

Nanticoke R.

Rappahannock Falls

Rappahannock R.

Potomac R.

Patuxent R.

Pocomoke R.

ancient ocean coastline

James R.

York R.

Falls of the James

where was it sealed?

Atlantic Ocean

Star Breach

Beacon?

Map drawn with the help of John Smith, 1612

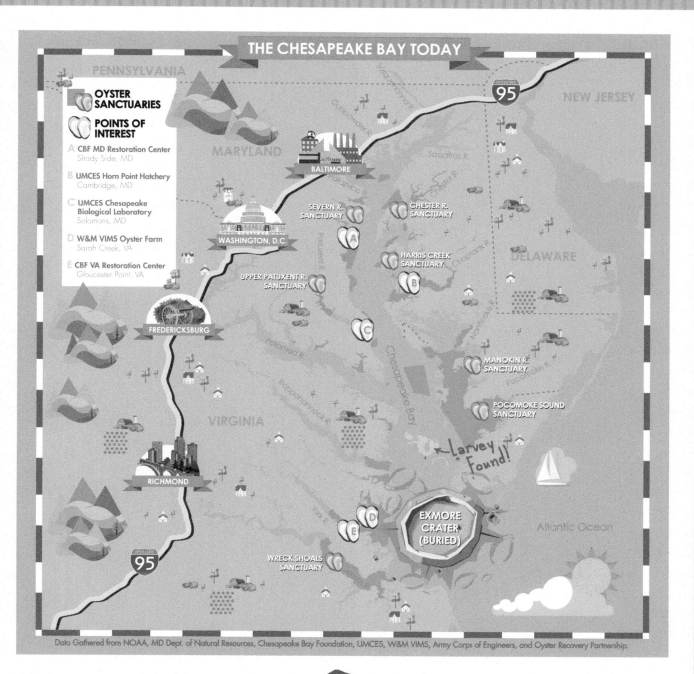

THE CHESAPEAKE BAY TODAY

OYSTER SANCTUARIES

POINTS OF INTEREST

A CBF MD Restoration Center
Shady Side, MD

B UMCES Horn Point Hatchery
Cambridge, MD

C UMCES Chesapeake
Biological Laboratory
Solomons, MD

D W&M VIMS Oyster Farm
Sarah Creek, VA

E CBF VA Restoration Center
Gloucester Point, VA

PENNSYLVANIA

NEW JERSEY

MARYLAND

95

Sassafras R.

Chester R.

BALTIMORE

Patapsco R.

SEVERN R.
SANCTUARY

CHESTER R.
SANCTUARY

DELAWARE

WASHINGTON, D.C.

A

Patuxent R.

HARRIS CREEK
SANCTUARY

B

Choptank R.

UPPER PATUXENT R.
SANCTUARY

C

Chesapeake Bay

FREDERICKSBURG

Potomac R.

MANOKIN R.
SANCTUARY

Pocomoke R.

Rappahannock R.

POCOMOKE SOUND
SANCTUARY

VIRGINIA

Larvey
Found!

RICHMOND

York R.

D

E

EXMORE
CRATER
(BURIED)

Atlantic Ocean

95

WRECK SHOALS
SANCTUARY

Data Gathered from NOAA, MD Dept. of Natural Resources, Chesapeake Bay Foundation, UMCES, W&M VIMS, Army Corps of Engineers, and Oyster Recovery Partnership.

Special thanks to CarolineMcKay.com for assitance with illustrations,
my friends for their support and volunteer contributions,
my family for their endless love and encouragement,
and my sweetheart for being the best companion a mermaid could wish for.

ISBN-10: 0-9990602-1-X
ISBN-13: 978-0-9990602-1-6

The Chesapeake Mermaid &
The Last Bivalvian

Story by The Chesapeake Mermaid

Illustrated by Angela Rose Mitchell

You may have heard oysters are the key to improving the Chesapeake Bay, and that's true. Have you ever thought it odd these ecological heroes resemble pet rocks? No, they're not rocks. Oysters are animals, and there's much more to their story hidden deep in the past. This is a tale that will change your opinion of oysters forever, and it comes from a creature old enough to remember.

The area where we live today was once an ancient ocean full of all kinds of creatures who lived in harmony. There was wildlife like we see today and magical beings and a world big enough for everything in between.

Changes began when a star fell to Earth and exploded in the sky with a thunderous roar. The impact of this event blew a deep hole in the ancient ocean. Everything began to fall into this star breach - the land, the water, everything. Something had to be done to restore the balance.

The solution arrived on waves of music. The Merfolk, masters of natural engineering, played an enchanted marsh organ, controlling the sea level through melody, and trapping the water in ice. The magical Bivalvians sang along in chorus while constructing themselves into fantastic structures. These larger relatives of today's oysters could unify into any shape, but they didn't have to settle in one place their entire lives. They could move again and again provided they had enough magic. Together, they were a force of nature adding stability to the fragile world around them.

The salty ocean water disappeared deep underground creating a vast lake frozen in time. Some believe the largest marine creatures ever seen were sealed inside this secret realm and are waiting to return.

In a crescendo of noble elements, the Merfolk and the magical Bivalvians guided the mighty Susquehanna River on its way to the Atlantic Ocean. This rush of freshwater carved towering waterfalls along the former coastline where our modern cities are today. This all happened very fast in geological time, but to everyone else, it was a very long song.

11

As the final note echoed across the shallow river valley, the ice melted away revealing a broad nursery where the sunlight and temperature were always just right. This natural wonder is now known as the Chesapeake Bay.

Here, billions of magical Bivalvians took the form of elaborate underwater castles attracting a court of creatures from across the region. There were columns reaching to the surface like outstretched arms and the Merfolk welcomed a cavalcade of characters to their new aquatic home.

Everyone who entered understood there were rules to live by and ways to take care of the world. Legends say they were written in some type of instruction manual understood by all languages of the region.

For a long, long time things were well. The Chesapeake Bay was a fairytale come true - the largest body of water of its kind in the entire world and a marvel of natural engineering. The marsh organ kept the sea level at the correct height, the star breach remained stable and sealed, and the creatures all sang in harmony.

This was a golden era when a curious mermaid came into the world. She loved to hear adventure stories about her home in the Chesapeake Bay from a time before she was born. She knew it was important for the future to learn as much as she could about the past.

Unfortunately, a dark chapter in this region was just beginning.

First came the Storm Waters. While thunderstorms moved across the sky, dark clouds of pollution and red waves of algae rolled into the bay. Many larger creatures like sea turtles, seals, and the Merfolk could no longer breathe.

The Merfolk gave a tearful goodbye to their bay family as they migrated with the larger animals to open waters in the Atlantic. Believing one day the bay would be safe enough for them to be summoned home, they left behind a magical beacon. However, during this upset many things were lost including the instructions for the bay and the knowledge of the ancients.

While this was occurring, the curious mermaid was separated from her family. She learned to live on her own with help from the wildlife and friendly humans.

The community of Bivalvians protected the remaining aquatic creatures by filtering the water and sheltering them from the storms. Working so hard to make the water livable drained the Bivalvians of their precious magic. Without their magic, the Bivalvians were unable to move and a sitting target for what was to come.

In this new era of sights and sounds came hungry mechanical beasts called Dredgers. These clumsy invaders from afar ate everything in sight and destroyed the beautiful Bivalvian structures in their search for food. For hundreds of years, they relentlessly attacked under the veil of darkness and stole in great numbers, leaving no time for recovery. The local humans fought back but they were no match for these lumbering metal dragons.

Over time, the bay creatures diminished in strength and lost their magic. The Storm Waters came often and the Dredgers took the biggest and strongest. The Bivalvian community and its ability to communicate destroyed, their song was silenced. Those that were left drifted farther and farther apart until all of the magical Bivalvians were gone.

This left only the common oysters we know today. Their old magic depleted, they struggle to protect the other creatures. For so long they had stood strong and helped others. Now they are waiting for help themselves.

The curious mermaid remained in the bay, working to restore the balance and help the creatures who grew up around her. She didn't know where the Chesapeake Merfolk had gone or how many were left. She would explore the watershed searching for pieces of the history she once knew. Perhaps one day she would find where the star breach was sealed, the enchanted marsh organ, and the beacon to summon the Merfolk home again.

The humans spotted her from time to time and named her "The Chesapeake Mermaid" since her real name could only be pronounced by the creatures under water. She would likely have remained a legend had she not discovered something which changed everything.

Not long ago, while exploring the bay, The Chesapeake Mermaid found an animal in distress. It was the last remaining magical Bivalvian! She named him Larvey because his fluffy old face resembled a baby oyster.

Larvey survived because he had a very special purpose - he KNOWS the ancient instructions for caring for the Chesapeake Bay. The legend had led us to believe the instructions were in a book, but like everything else in the ancient world, the key was in oysters.

Larvey was used to sticking to his oyster friends, so he enjoys sitting on top of the Chesapeake Mermaid's head and giving her pearls of wisdom from time to time. She takes care of him because there aren't many creatures left from before the Dredgers who know how to care for a magical Bivalvian.

Larvey's had a rough life and his memory isn't always reliable, but he's in good spirits and his will is strong. His knowledge of how the things had once been can help us today, but we can't turn back time. Like the rest of the oysters, Larvey is looking to us for new magic.

The recipe for magic includes hope and happiness, but we need something stronger to bring balance to the bay right now and for the future. Humans have a powerful magic called science. Some of you might have science already, but for those who are new, we can learn together.

Your journey has already begun! Larvey shared this story with the Chesapeake Mermaid so she could share it with you. Now you've already learned so much about the Chesapeake Bay.

Friendly people like you are already working to restore oyster reefs and keep our water cleaner. Together we can restore the magic and build a new community. And for the oysters, that will be enough to sing about!

The Bay will never be the same as the past, but it doesn't have to be the same to be a wonderful place where everything is in harmony. Let's work together to learn, solve problems, and write new instructions for now and the future.

Science

FUN FACTS TO EXPLORE

Oysters

- Animals called bivalves which grow in reef colonies
- Filter the water as they eat, reducing pollution
- Grow together in rough shapes creating homes for animals
- Reef restoration varies and can include blocks called reef balls, layer cakes, reef castles and more
- Baby oysters, called larvae, can swim using tiny hairs, called cilia, until they find a place to stay their entire lives

Marsh Organ

- Instruments of science used to study sea level rise
- Shows us how grasses respond differently to soil, air, and water
- Tubes containing the grasses are stacked side by side in steps resembling the musical instrument

Science

Exmore Crater

- Natural depression on the lower part of the Chesapeake Bay
- Created 35 million years ago by a meteor
- Affects the stability of the Chesapeake region today
- Water below the crater has nearly twice the salt of today's ocean

Storm Water

- Polluted runoff from land into the bay caused by storms
- Too many chemicals can cause extra algae to bloom, blocking light and absorbing oxygen needed for plants and animals

Dredgers

- Tools or machines used to move or remove underwater targets
- Used for a long time to farm oysters and clear channels before rules were created and enforced

What You Can Do

- Explore our environment and get outside often
- Reduce, reuse and recycle to cut down on garbage and pollution
- Volunteer for a beach or park cleanup effort
- Build a rain garden in your yard or community
- Support restaurants contributing to oyster reef restoration
- Become a member of our bay organizations and local parks
- Respect wildlife and report lost, injured, or unusual animals
- Take pictures but leave feathers, shells, or flowers where you find them
- Attend festivals and events supporting our bay organizations
- Keep drains that lead directly to the bay clear of debris and trash
- Eat local seafood and buy from local farmers
- Swim and fish in areas with proper permission
- **Follow the Chesapeake Mermaid on social media**

ABOUT THE CHESAPEAKE MERMAID

The Chesapeake Mermaid makes appearances at events throughout the region. She invites us to explore the Chesapeake watershed on a quest for innovative solutions to the natural world's toughest problems. She is a leader among volunteers and encourages the public to get involved in environmental programs. Become a part of her journey at chesapeakemermaid.com or summon her to an event by writing to info@chesapeakemermaid.com

Watch for other great adventures from The Chesapeake Mermaid

ChesapeakeMermaid.com

Ooo ooo ooo
Ahh ahh ahh

The oysters have a song.
They sing it in the bay.
The people came,
But couldn't hear,
And now it's gone away.

Ooo ooo ooo
Ahh ahh ahh

We can bring it back.
Let's do all we can.
One change can make,
A difference,
In water, air, and land.

Ooo ooo ooo
Ahh ahh ahh

One change can make,
A difference,
In water, air, and land.

CPSIA information can be obtained
at www.ICGtesting.com
Printed in the USA
BVOW05s2135040617

485935BV00003B/4/P